THE MAGIC OF NUMBERS

THE MAGIC
OF NUMBERS

Compiled by

SYDNEY H. LAMB

ARC BOOKS, INC.
New York

Published by ARC BOOKS, Inc.

219 Park Avenue South, New York, N.Y. 10003

Library of Congress Catalog Card Number 67-10616

Printed in U.S.A.

CONTENTS

SECTION ONE

NUMBER PATTERNS

$$9 \times 9 = 81$$
$$99 \times 99 = 9,801$$
$$999 \times 999 = 998,001$$
$$9,999 \times 9,999 = 99,980,001$$
$$99,999 \times 99,999 = 9,999,800,001$$
$$999,999 \times 999,999 = 999,998,000,001$$
$$9,999,999 \times 9,999,999 = 99,999,980,000,001$$

$$999,999 \times 2 = 1,999,998$$
$$999,999 \times 3 = 2,999,997$$
$$999,999 \times 4 = 3,999,996$$
$$999,999 \times 5 = 4,999,995$$
$$999,999 \times 6 = 5,999,994$$
$$999,999 \times 7 = 6,999,993$$
$$999,999 \times 8 = 7,999,992$$
$$999,999 \times 9 = 8,999,991$$

$$0 \times 9 + 8 = 8$$
$$9 \times 9 + 7 = 88$$
$$98 \times 9 + 6 = 888$$
$$987 \times 9 + 5 = 8,888$$
$$9,876 \times 9 + 4 = 88,888$$
$$98,765 \times 9 + 3 = 888,888$$
$$987,654 \times 9 + 2 = 8,888,888$$
$$9,876,543 \times 9 + 1 = 88,888,888$$
$$98,765,432 \times 9 + 0 = 888,888,888$$

$$0 \times 9 + 1 = 1$$
$$1 \times 9 + 2 = 11$$
$$12 \times 9 + 3 = 111$$
$$123 \times 9 + 4 = 1,111$$
$$1,234 \times 9 + 5 = 11,111$$
$$12,345 \times 9 + 6 = 111,111$$
$$123,456 \times 9 + 7 = 1,111,111$$
$$1,234,567 \times 9 + 8 = 11,111,111$$
$$12,345,678 \times 9 + 9 = 111,111,111$$

$$1 \times 8 + 1 = 9$$
$$12 \times 8 + 2 = 98$$
$$123 \times 8 + 3 = 987$$
$$1,234 \times 8 + 4 = 9,876$$
$$12,345 \times 8 + 5 = 98,765$$
$$123,456 \times 8 + 6 = 987,654$$
$$1,234,567 \times 8 + 7 = 9,876,543$$
$$12,345,678 \times 8 + 8 = 98,765,432$$
$$123,456,789 \times 8 + 9 = 987,654,321$$

$$11 \times 11 = 121$$
$$111 \times 111 = 12,321$$
$$1,111 \times 1,111 = 1,234,321$$
$$11,111 \times 11,111 = 123,454,321$$
$$111,111 \times 111,111 = 12,345,654,321$$
$$1,111,111 \times 1,111,111 = 1,234,567,654,321$$
$$11,111,111 \times 11,111,111 = 123,456,787,654,321$$
$$111,111,111 \times 111,111,111 = 12,345,678,987,654,321$$

$$12,345,679 \times 9 \ = 111,111,111$$
$$12,345,679 \times 18 = 222,222,222$$
$$12,345,679 \times 27 = 333,333,333$$
$$12,345,679 \times 36 = 444,444,444$$
$$12,345,679 \times 45 = 555,555,555$$
$$12,345,679 \times 54 = 666,666,666$$
$$12,345,679 \times 63 = 777,777,777$$
$$12,345,679 \times 72 = 888,888,888$$
$$12,345,679 \times 81 = 999,999,999$$

If the numbers from 1 to 9 inclusive, but omitting 8, be used as a multiplicand, and any one of them multiplied by 9 be used as a multiplier, the result will present a succession of figures the same as that multiplied by the 9, as above.

$$123,456,789 \times 8 = 987,654,312$$
$$987,654,312 + 9 = 987,654,321$$

If we want to multiply a three-place number by 1,001 we need not work it out, but just write the number twice and we get the answer.

Thus: $643 \times 1,001$ is $643,643$

Any three-place number written twice so that it becomes a six-place number (as above) is divisible by 7, 11, and 13.

For instance: 643,643 divided by 7 is 91,949
643,643 divided by 11 is 58,513
643,643 divided by 13 is 49,511

THE NUMBERS 1 TO 9

$$1 \times 1 = 1^2$$
$$2 \times 2 = 2^2$$
$$3 \times 3 = 3^2$$
$$4 \times 4 = 4^2$$
$$5 \times 5 = 5^2$$
$$6 \times 6 = 6^2$$
$$7 \times 7 = 7^2$$
$$8 \times 8 = 8^2$$
$$9 \times 9 = 9^2$$

$$1 = 1$$
$$1 + 2 + 1 = 2 + 2$$
$$1 + 2 + 3 + 2 + 1 = 3 + 3 + 3$$
$$1 + 2 + 3 + 4 + 3 + 2 + 1 = 4 + 4 + 4 + 4$$
$$1 + 2 + 3 + 4 + 5 + 4 + 3 + 2 + 1 = 5 + 5 + 5 + 5 + 5$$
$$1 + 2 + 3 + 4 + 5 + 6 + 5 + 4 + 3 + 2 + 1 = 6 + 6 + 6 + 6 + 6 + 6$$
$$1 + 2 + 3 + 4 + 5 + 6 + 7 + 6 + 5 + 4 + 3 + 2 + 1 = 7 + 7 + 7 + 7 + 7 + 7 + 7$$
$$1 + 2 + 3 + 4 + 5 + 6 + 7 + 8 + 7 + 6 + 5 + 4 + 3 + 2 + 1 = 8 + 8 + 8 + 8 + 8 + 8 + 8 + 8$$
$$1 + 2 + 3 + 4 + 5 + 6 + 7 + 8 + 9 + 8 + 7 + 6 + 5 + 4 + 3 + 2 + 1 = 9 + 9 + 9 + 9 + 9 + 9 + 9 + 9 + 9$$

$$1 + 2 + 3 + 4 + 5 + 6 + 7 + 8 + 9 = 45 : 4 + 5 = 9$$

PECULIAR PROPERTIES OF CERTAIN NUMBERS

The number 37 is one which, being multiplied by each of the figures of arithmetical progression, 3, 6, 9, 12, 15, 18, 21, 24, 27, all the products which result from it are composed of three repetitions of the same figure; and the sum of these figures is equal to that by which you multiplied the 37.

37	37	37	37	37	37	37	37	37
3	6	9	12	15	18	21	24	27
111	222	333	444	555	666	777	888	999

Another very curious number is 142,857. If this number is multiplied by 2, 3, 4, 5, 6 the result gives the same figures in the same order, but beginning at a different point, and when multiplied by 7 the result consists of all nines.

142,857	142,857	142,857	142,857	142,857	142,857
2	3	4	5	6	7
285,714	428,571	571,428	714,285	857,142	999,999

142,857 multiplied by 8 = 1,142,856. Add the first figure to the last one and you have 142,857, the original number with the figures the same as at the start.

Here are two more peculiar numbers.

$$1,089 \times 1 = 1,089$$
$$1,089 \times 2 = 2,178$$
$$1,089 \times 3 = 3,267$$
$$1,089 \times 4 = 4,356$$
$$1,089 \times 5 = 5,445$$
$$1,089 \times 6 = 6,534$$
$$1,089 \times 7 = 7,623$$
$$1,089 \times 8 = 8,712$$
$$1,089 \times 9 = 9,801$$

Note how the digits of the first two columns increase, whereas in columns three and four they decrease.

Note also that $1,089 \times 9$ is this number in reverse.

$$76,923 \times 1 = 76,923$$
$$76,923 \times 10 = 769,230$$
$$76,923 \times 9 = 692,307$$
$$76,923 \times 12 = 923,076$$
$$76,923 \times 3 = 230,769$$
$$76,923 \times 4 = 307,692$$

$$76,923 \times 2 = 153,846$$
$$76,923 \times 7 = 538,461$$
$$76,923 \times 5 = 384,615$$
$$76,923 \times 11 = 846,153$$
$$76,923 \times 6 = 461,538$$
$$76,923 \times 8 = 615,384$$

Note that the results give the same figures in the same order, but beginning at a different point.

Note also that every row and column adds up to 27.

The decimal equivalents of $\frac{1}{7}$, $\frac{2}{7}$, $\frac{3}{7}$, $\frac{4}{7}$, $\frac{5}{7}$, $\frac{6}{7}$, each contain the same series of figures, but starting at a different point thus:

.142857 .285714 .428571 .571428 .714285 .857142

The decimal equivalents of $\frac{1}{13}$, $\frac{3}{13}$, $\frac{4}{13}$, $\frac{9}{13}$, $\frac{10}{13}$, $\frac{12}{13}$, also contain the same series of figures, but starting at a different point, thus:

.076923 .230769 .307692 .692307 .769230 .923076

Similarly, the decimal equivalents of $\frac{2}{13}$, $\frac{5}{13}$, $\frac{6}{13}$, $\frac{7}{13}$, $\frac{8}{13}$, $\frac{11}{13}$ contain the same series of figures, but starting at a different point, thus:

.153846 .384615 .461538 .538461 .615384 .846153

NINE is the most fascinating and versatile of numbers. (See Section One on Number Patterns.)

When multiplied by the numbers 1 to 9 inclusive the resulting figures always add up to 9. Thus:

$$9 \times 2 = 18 \quad 1 + 8 = 9$$
$$9 \times 3 = 27 \quad 2 + 7 = 9$$
$$9 \times 4 = 36 \quad 3 + 6 = 9$$
$$9 \times 5 = 45 \quad 4 + 5 = 9$$
$$9 \times 6 = 54 \quad 5 + 4 = 9$$
$$9 \times 7 = 63 \quad 6 + 3 = 9$$
$$9 \times 8 = 72 \quad 7 + 2 = 9$$
$$9 \times 9 = 81 \quad 8 + 1 = 9$$

Note how the tens increase and the units decrease progressively.

$$18 + 27 + 36 + 45 + 54 + 63 + 72 + 81 = 396$$
$$18 = 1 + 8 = 9$$

If you take any row of figures and, reversing their order, subtract one from the other, the digits of the answer added together will always be nine.

Example:

```
  2,941
  1,492
  ─────
  1,449   1 + 4 + 4 + 9 = 18    1 + 8 = 9
```

Write down any number and subtract the sum of its digits, and no matter what figures you started with, the digits of the answer will always total 9.

Example:

```
7,549,132 (7 + 5 + 4 + 9 + 1 + 3 + 2 = 31)
       31
─────────
7,549,101 the digits of which add up to 27: 2 + 7 = 9
```

A similar result is obtained if you raise the numbers so changed to their squares and cubes.

For instance: 62 reversed gives 26. Subtract 26 from 62 and you have 36: 3 + 6 = 9.

Now, the squares of 26 and 62 respectively are 676 and 3,844. Subtract one from the other and you get 3,168, the digits of which added together total 18: 1 + 8 = 9.

The cubes of 26 and 62 are 17,576 and 238,328. On subtracting, the result is 220,752; add these digits together and the result is 18: 1 + 8 = 9.

Every square number necessarily ends with one of these five figures—1, 4, 5, 6, 9.

Every square number is divisible by 3 or becomes so when diminished by unity (1).

Thus:

2 × 2 = 4	4 less 1 = 3	
4 × 4 = 16	16 less 1 = 15	15 ÷ 3 = 5
11 × 11 = 121	121 less 1 = 120	120 ÷ 3 = 40

Every square number is divisible also by 4 or becomes so when diminished by unity (1).

Thus:

3 × 3 = 9	9 less 1 = 8	8 ÷ 4 = 2
12 × 12 = 144		144 ÷ 4 = 36
15 × 15 = 225	225 less 1 = 224	224 ÷ 4 = 56
27 × 27 = 729	729 less 1 = 728	728 ÷ 4 = 182

Every square number is divisible also by 5 or becomes so when increased or decreased by unity (1).

Thus:

6 × 6 = 36	36 less 1 = 35	35 ÷ 5 = 7
7 × 7 = 49	49 plus 1 = 50	50 ÷ 5 = 10
13 × 13 = 169	169 plus 1 = 170	170 ÷ 5 = 34
24 × 24 = 576	576 less 1 = 575	575 ÷ 5 = 115

In any number consisting of four consecutive figures the two end figures, when multiplied together and subtracted from the result of multiplying the two center figures, will always have a difference of two.

Thus:

1,234	1 × 4 = 4	2 × 3 = 6	6 − 4 = 2
5,678	5 × 8 = 40	6 × 7 = 42	42 − 40 = 2
6,789	6 × 9 = 54	7 × 8 = 56	56 − 54 = 2

SECTION THREE

TESTS FOR DIVISIBILITY OF NUMBERS

---

1. Any *even* number is divisible by 2.

2. If the sum of the number is divisible by 3 the number itself is divisible by 3.

E.g. 45,264 is divisible by 3 because the sum of the digits $4 + 5 + 2 + 6 + 4 = 21$ is divisible by 3.

3. If the last two digits of a number are divisible by 4 the number is divisible by 4.

E.g. 45,264. The last two digits form the number 64, which is easily recognizable as being divisible by 4. Hence the whole number is divisible by 4.

4. Any number the last digit of which is 5 or 0 is divisible by 5.

5. If a number is *even* and the sum of its digits is divisible by 3, then the number is divisible by 6.

E.g. 45,264 is divisible by 6 because the sum of its digits $4 + 5 + 2 + 6 + 4$ add up to 21, which is divisible by 3.

6. There is no simple rule regarding the divisibility of 7.

7. If the last three digits of a number are divisible by 8, then the number is divisible by 8.

E.g. 9,872

The last three digits, 872, are divisible by 8 (109), therefore the whole number is divisible by 8.

8. If the sum of a number is divisible by 9 the whole number is divisible by 9.

E.g. 1,107 is divisible by 9 because the sum of its digits $1 + 1 + 0 + 7 = 9$ is divisible by 9.

9. If a number's last digit is 0 the number is divisible by 10.

10. A number is divisible by 11 if the difference in the sums of its *alternate* digits is either zero or a multiple of 11.

E.g. 142,857

The difference in the sums of the alternate digits $= (1 + 2 + 5) \sim (4 + 8 + 7) = 8 \sim 19 = 11$.
Therefore 142,857 is divisible by 11 (*i.e.* 12,987).

E.g. 13,981

The difference in the sums of the alternate digits $= (1 + 9 + 1) \sim (3 + 8) = 11 \sim 11 = 0$.
Therefore 13,981 is divisible by 11 (*i.e.* 1,271).

11. A number is divisible by 12 if the sum of its digits is divisible by 3 and if its last two digits form a number which is divisible by 4, *i.e.*, if the number satisfies the divisibility tests for 4 and 3, then the number will be divisible by 12.

  E.g. 14,964 is divisible by 3 because the sum of its digits, 24, is divisible by 3; also the last two digits form the number 64, which is divisible by 4. Hence the number itself is divisible by 12 (*i.e.*, 1,247).

12. The above test—No. 11—can be extended to cover other tests.

  E.g. A number is divisible by 33 if it satisfies the tests for divisibility by 3 and 11.

13. A number which consists of the same digit repeated six times is divisible by 3, 7, 11, and 13.

  E.g. 111,111 is divisible by 3 = 37,037
  111,111 is divisible by 7 = 15,873
  111,111 is divisible by 11 = 10,101
  111,111 is divisible by 13 = 8,547

SECTION FOUR

MULTIPLICATION METHODS OF THE PAST

An Old Method of Multiplication
(At one time used by Russian peasants)

To multiply 654 by 456

Form two columns headed by the multiplicand and multiplier. The number in the left column is progressively divided by two, ignoring any remainders, and the right column at the same time multiplied by two. This operation is continued until number one is reached in the left column.

Cross out all even numbers in the left column and also even numbers in the same line in the right column. The remaining numbers in the right-hand column, when added together, will give the answer to the multiplication.

~~654~~	~~456~~			
327	912	912		
163	1,824	1,824		
81	3,648	3,648		
~~40~~	~~7,296~~		*Proof:*	654
~~20~~	~~14,592~~			456
~~10~~	~~29,184~~			———
5	58,368	58,368		3,924
~~2~~	~~116,736~~			3,270·
1	233,472	233,472		2,616·
		———		———
		298,224		298,224

21

The Lattice Method of Multiplying

This method was taught in England about 400 years ago.

To multiply 123 by 456

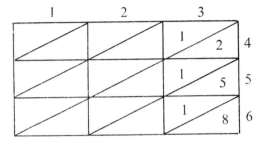

Stage 1. Multiply the 3 by 6 squares to obtain 18, placing the units to the right of the diagonal line and the tens above the slant lines, as shown in the diagram.

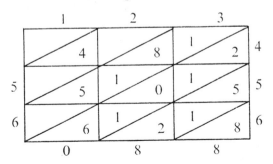

Stage 2. Multiply the 2 by 6 squares, placing the result as above.

Stage 3. Multiply the 1 by 6 squares, placing the result as above.

Stage 4. The answer is obtained by adding the figures together in the diagonal columns, starting with the bottom right-hand column which has only one figure, *i.e.*, 8.

The next diagonal column adds up to 8.

The next diagonal column adds up to 10— place the 0 down and carry the 1 to the next column.

After all the diagonal columns have been added and placed on the bottom and on the left-hand side, you merely read the number appearing for the answer—namely, *56,088.*

To Multiply 1,234 by 567

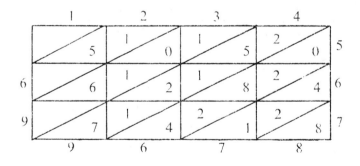

Answer: 699,678

To multiply 2,345 by 6,789

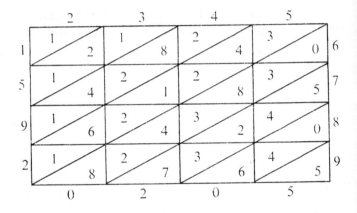

Answer: 15,920,205

SECTION FIVE

HOW MANY IS A MILLION?

A million seconds = 11 days 13 hours 46 minutes and 40 seconds

A million ounces = 31 tons 500 lbs.

A million pints = 125,000 gallons

A million inches = 15 miles 1377 yards 2⅓ feet

A million cents = $10,000.00

A million is a thousand thousands = 1 with 6 zeros

A billion is a thousand millions = 1 with 9 zeros

A trillion is a million millions = 1 with 12 zeros

A quadrillion is a thousand trillions = 1 with 15 zeros

A quintillion is a thousand quadrillions = 1 with 18 zeros

A sextillion is a thousand quintillions = 1 with 21 zeros

A million days are about equal to 2,700 years. Thus, since the birth of Christ, a million days have not elapsed.

How long would it take to count a million objects if it takes a second to count one object?

There are sixty seconds in one minute and sixty minutes in one hour, making 3,600 seconds in an hour. Therefore 3,600 objects can be counted in one hour. To count one million objects would take, therefore, $\frac{1,000,000}{3,600}$ hours, or approximately 278 hours, or 11 days and 14 hours of non-stop counting.

Now, suppose that only 8 hours are spent each day in counting, and providing that you worked like a clock (including Sundays and holidays), to count the million objects would take you 34 days and 6 hours.

Take the number 15 and multiply it by itself, and you get 225. Now multiply 225 by itself and so on until fifteen products have been multiplied by themselves in turn. The final product would contain 38,589 figures, and allowing, say, four figures to an inch, the answer would be about 800 feet long.

To work out this apparently simple sum would require about 500,000,000 figures. If they could be worked out at the rate of four a minute, a person working ten hours a day would take nearly seven years to complete the sum if he worked 300 days a year.

SECTION SIX

PUZZLES

For answers, *see* SECTION ELEVEN, p. 59.

---

1. Write each of the numbers 1 to 10, using each of the ten digits just once, to equal 1.

2. Write each of the numbers 1 to 10, using each of the ten digits just once, to equal 100.

3. Write 31 using only the digit 3 five times.

4. Take away half of thirteen and let eight remain.

5. From 45 take 45 and let 45 remain.

6. Divide two by five so that the result will be a thousand.

7. Using the nine digits once each, write a fraction equal to $\frac{1}{2}$.

8. Using each of the numbers from 1 to 9 once only, write them in such a way that they total 99,999.

9. Which is the heavier, a pound of feathers or a pound of gold?

10. Rearrange nine matches to make ten.

11. Rearrange six matches to make nothing.

12. How can you use eight 8's to make a total of 1,000?

13. How can you use seven 4's to make 100?

14. How can you use sixteen 4's to make a total of 1,000?

15. How can you make 100 by using six 9's?

16. Is six dozen dozen greater than, equal to, or less than half a dozen dozen?

17. How can you write 24 with three equal digits, none of them being 8?

18. Arrange three 8's so that they equal 7.

SECTION SEVEN

PROBLEMS

For answers, *see* SECTION ELEVEN, p. 59.

---

19. Tom and Henry were playing at marbles, and Tom said to Henry, "If you give me one of your marbles I'll have as many as you." Henry replied, "You give me one of your marbles, and I'll have twice as many as you."

How many marbles did each have?

20. If you can saw off a piece of a tree trunk 12 feet long in one minute, how long will it take you to saw it into twelve equal pieces?

21. A sheep farmer, on being asked how many sheep he had, replied that if one-fifth, one-sixth, and one-seventh of the flock were added together he would have 107.

How many sheep did he have?

22. If you double $\frac{1}{5}$ of a fraction and multiply it by that fraction, you would get $\frac{1}{10}$. What is the original fraction?

23. I am a booking clerk at a station. There are 25 stations on my part of the line, and different tickets for each station up and down the line.

How many different kinds of tickets do you think I have to keep at my booking office?

24. A father agreed to give his son 10¢ for each problem in arithmetic he got right at school, but the son had to pay his father 5¢ for each incorrect answer. At the end of the school term 120 problems had been done, and neither of them owed anything to the other.

How many problems did the boy solve correctly?

25. A plane takes 1 hour 20 minutes to fly from place A to place B and only 80 minutes to return. Why?

26. When twelve is subtracted from a certain number the result is exactly the same as when that number is subtracted from twelve. What is the number?

27. Which number is twice the product of its digits?

28. Which number is three times the sum of its digits?

29. If a brick balances evenly in the scales with three quarters of a pound and three quarters of a brick, what is the weight of the whole brick?

30. A farmer's wife drove to the market to sell a basket of eggs.

To her first customer she sold half her eggs and half an egg. To the second customer she sold half of what remained in her basket and half an egg. To the third customer she sold half of what remained in her basket and half an egg. And to her last customer she sold half of what remained in her basket and half an egg. She was then left with eight eggs.

How many eggs did she start out with, and how many eggs did each customer buy? She did not break any eggs in supplying her customers.

31. A brick weighs six pounds plus one-half of its total weight. What is its total weight?

32. With only the weights of 1, 2, 4, 8, 16, and 32 lb., any weight between one and sixty-three lb. can be given.

33. Similarly, any weight between one and forty lb. can be given with weights of 1, 3, 9, and 27 lb.

34. A farmer bought two machines to use on his farm. Afterwards he found that they would not serve the purpose for which he wanted them. He sold them for $600 each, making a loss of 20% on one of them and a profit of 20% on the other. How much did each machine cost him, and did he lose or gain on the transaction?

35. A farmer took his horse to the blacksmith to be shod. The blacksmith said he would do it if the farmer would agree to pay one penny for the first nail and double for each subsequent nail. As there were six nails for each of the four shoes, how much had the farmer to pay?

36. One Christmas a businessman decided to distribute $100 among his 100 employees in such a manner that each man received $3, each woman $2, and each junior 50¢. How many men, women, and juniors were there, there being employed five times as many women as men?

37. A bottle and a cork cost $1.10. The bottle cost $1.00 more than the cork. What was the cost of each?

38. A Bedouin dies leaving 17 horses to his three sons. To the eldest he leaves one-half of his horses, to the next one he leaves one-third of his horses, and to the youngest son he leaves one-ninth. A dispute arises as to how the will can be carried out without sacrificing one of the horses. The matter is referred to a dervish to settle the dispute. How does he manage it?

39. A wine vendor has to divide the contents of an eight-quart wine cask into two equal parts using only the cask and two empty jugs with capacities of 5 quarts and 3 quarts respectively. How can he do this?

40. A young lady went into a post office and putting seventy-five cents on the counter said to the assistant, "Please give me some two-cent stamps, six times as many one-cent stamps, and make up the rest of the money in five-cent stamps." How many of each did she receive?

41. In offering two youths a job a businessman told them he would start them at $200 a year, $100 to be paid every half year. He promised them their salary would be raised if their work proved satisfactory. They could have a raise of $30 per year, or if they preferred it $10 each half year. One youth said he would accept the increase of $30 per year, while the other youth agreed to have the raise of $10 half-yearly. Which youth was the gainer and by how much?

WHAT ARE THE MISSING NUMBERS?

42.	2	4	7	11	16	—	—	—
43.	2	5	10	17	26	—	—	—
44.	180	175	165	150	130	—	—	—
45.	254	252	248	240	224	—	—	—
46.	2	4	8	16	32	—	—	—
47.	2	4	12	48	240	—	—	—
48.	32	16	8	4	2	—	—	—
49.	2,187	729	243	81	27	—	—	—

REPLACE THE x WITH THE MISSING NUMBER

Addition

50. x23x
    4xx1
    ―――
    x5x5

51. 1x1
    2xx
    x42
    3xx
    ―――
    x9x

Subtraction

52. 5xx8
    x36x
    ―――
    x11x

53. 6x5x
    x7x3
    ―――
    5xx

Multiplication

54.
```
    ×8
    3x
   ───
   xx2
  1xx·
  ─────
  1x82
```

55.
```
   3xx6
    x8x
  ──────
  3xx04
  2x6x8·
  2xx92·
  ───────
  2x2xx84
```

Division

56.
```
5x)1xxx(x8
   x5x
   ───
   xxx
   xxx
   ───
   ···
```

57.
```
2xx)3x1x5(1x3
    2xx
    ────
    1x6x
    1xx5
    ─────
     x4x
     x4x
     ────
     ···
```

SECTION EIGHT

GAMES

Ask someone to open a book at any page, and to choose any word in one of the first nine lines on the page, then to make a note of that word and close the book. Then ask him:

1. To double the number of the page and multiply by 5.
2. Add 25.
3. Add the line number and multiply by 10.
4. Add the number of the word in the line.
5. Subtract 250 and then give you the result.
6. This result will give you the number of the page, the number of the line, and the number of the word, in that order.

Example:

Suppose the word "Puzzle" is the word chosen and is the sixth word on line five of page twenty-four of the book.

1. Double the number of the page and multiply by five—*i.e.* $48 \times 5 = 240$.
2. Add $25 = 265$.
3. Add the line number and multiply by 10. $265 + 5 = 270$. $270 \times 10 = 2,700$.
4. Add the number of the word in the line. $2,700 + 6 = 2,706$.
5. Subtract 250. $2,706 - 250 = 2,456$.
6. Page 24; line 5; word 6.

Ask a friend to think of a number between 1 and 63. To find out the number he has thought of, ask him in which columns of the following table the number appears.

Add together the numbers at the head of these columns, and the total gives the number first thought of.

32	16	8	4	2	1	32	16	8	4	2	1
32	16	8	4	2	1	48	48	40	36	34	33
33	17	9	5	3	3	49	49	41	37	35	35
34	18	10	6	6	5	50	50	42	38	38	37
35	19	11	7	7	7	51	51	43	39	39	39
36	20	12	12	10	9	52	52	44	44	42	41
37	21	13	13	11	11	53	53	45	45	43	43
38	22	14	14	14	13	54	54	46	46	46	45
39	23	15	15	15	15	55	55	47	47	47	47
40	24	24	20	18	17	56	56	56	52	50	49
41	25	25	21	19	19	57	57	57	53	51	51
42	26	26	22	22	21	58	58	58	54	54	53
43	27	27	23	23	23	59	59	59	55	55	55
44	28	28	28	26	25	60	60	60	60	58	57
45	29	29	29	27	27	61	61	61	61	59	59
46	30	30	30	30	29	62	62	62	62	62	61
47	31	31	31	31	31	63	63	63	63	63	63

E.g. Suppose the number thought of is 63. This number appears in the columns headed 32, 16, 8, 4, 2, 1, which added together total 63.

Ask someone to write down any number containing three figures diminishing in value.

Reverse and subtract.

Reverse this result and add.

The result will always be 1,089.

E.g.	765
Reverse =	567
Subtract =	198
Reverse =	891
Add =	1,089

TO FIND OUT THE NUMBER FIRST THOUGHT OF

1. Take any number with three figures but not alike.
2. Double it and add 4.
3. Multiply by 5 and add 12.
4. Multiply by 10 and subtract 320.
5. Cut off the last two figures, and the number left will be the one first thought of.

E.g. Suppose the number thought of is 123.

1. Double it and add 4. 246 + 4 = 250.
2. Multiply by 5 and add 12. 1,250 + 12 = 1,262.
3. Multiply by 10 and subtract 320. 12,620 − 320 = 12,300.
4. Cut off the last two figures, which then leaves 123 (*i.e.*, the number first thought of).

1. Ask a friend to think of a number; to multiply it by 2 and add 4.
2. Divide this by 2 and add 7.
3. Multiply by 8 and subtract 12.
4. Divide by 4 and subtract 11 and give the result.
5. From this result you subtract 4 and divide by 2, which will leave the number first thought of.

E.g. Suppose the number thought of is 55.
   1. Multiply by 2 and add 4. $110 + 4 = 114$.
   2. Divide this by 2 and add 7. $57 + 7 = 64$.
   3. Multiply by 8 and subtract 12. $512 - 12 = 500$.
   4. Divide by 4 and subtract 11. $125 - 11 = 114$.
   5. Subtract 4 and divide by 2. $110 \div 2 = 55$, which is the number first thought of.

TO FIND OUT THE LAST FOUR DIGITS OF A FRIEND'S TELEPHONE NUMBER

1. Take 60.
2. Divide by 2.
3. Add the last four digits of the telephone number.
4. Subtract 25.
5. Multiply by 3.
6. Subtract 15.
7. Multiply by 2.
8. Divide by 6.
9. The answer will be the last four digits of the telephone number.

Example:

Suppose the last four digits are 3579.

1. Take 60.
2. Divide by $2 = 30$.
3. Add last four digits of telephone number. $30 + 3,579 = 3,609$
4. Subtract 25. $3,609 - 25 = 3,584$
5. Multiply by 3. $3,584 \times 3 = 10,752$
6. Subtract 15. $10,752 - 15 = 10,737$
7. Multiply by 2. $10,737 \times 2 = 21,474$
8. Divide by 6. $21,474 \div 6 = 3,579$
9. The last four digits of the telephone number are 3579.

TO FIND THE AGE OF A PERSON AND ALSO THE NUMBER OF HIS HOUSE

1. Take the number of the house and double it.

2. Add 5.

3. Multiply by 50.

4. Add his age.

5. Add the number of days in the year.

6. Subtract 615.

7. The figures to the right of the result will give the age of the person and the remaining figures the number of his house.

Example:

Suppose the age of the person is 37 and the number of his house is 28.

1. Number of house is 28. $28 \times 2 = 56$.

2. Add 5. $56 + 5 = 61$.

3. Multiply by 50. $61 \times 50 = 3,050$.

4. Add his age. $3,050 + 37 = 3,087$.

5. Add the number of days in a year.

     $3,087 + 365 = 3,452$.

6. Subtract 615. $3,452 - 615 = 2,837$.

7. The figures to the right of the result give the age— *i.e.*, 37, and the figures to the left the number of the house—*i.e.*, 28.

TO FIND OUT HOW OLD A PERSON IS AND THE DATE OF HIS BIRTH

Ask the person to:

1. Multiply the number of the month of his birth by 100.
2. Add the date of the month.
3. Multiply this sum by 2.
4. Add 8.
5. Multiply this by 5.
6. Add 4.
7. Multiply this by 10.
8. Add 4.
9. Add his age to this.
10. From this result subtract 444.

Thus: Supposing the person was born on July 4th, 1917.

1. Multiply the number of the month by 100 = 700.
2. Add the date of the month. $700 + 4 = 704.$
3. Multiply this sum by 2. $704 \times 2 = 1,408.$
4. Add 8. $= 1,416.$
5. Multiply by 5. $1,416 \times 5 = 7,080.$
6. Add 4. $= 7,084.$
7. Multiply this sum by 10. $7,084 \times 10 = 70,840.$
8. Add 4. $= 70,844.$
9. Add his age—*i.e.*, 48 years $= 70,892.$
10. Subtract 444. $= 70,448.$

The final two figures give the age—*i.e.*, 48 years.

The next figure (or figures) gives the date of the month—*i.e.*, the 4th.

The next figure (or figures) gives the number of the month—*i.e.*, July.

Ask a friend to write down any two figures or sets of figures. Then request him to add them together, but without drawing a line underneath. Get him to put down another figure or set of figures, add them together, write the result down again, and continue this operation until there are ten sets of figures on the paper in one column. Now ask him to draw a line underneath and find the total. By multiplying the seventh line of figures by eleven you can obtain the total before your friend has had time to add up the ten lines of figures.

Examples:

	2	14	123	2,751
	3	21	130	3,840
2 + 3 =	5	35	253	6,591
5 + 3 =	8	56	383	10,431
8 + 5 =	13	91	636	17,022
13 + 8 =	21	147	1,019	27,453
21 + 13 =	34*	238*	1,655*	44,475*
34 + 21 =	55	385	2,674	71,928
55 + 34 =	89	623	4,329	116,403
89 + 55 =	144	1,008	7,003	188,331
	374	2,618	18,205	489,225

* represents line 7.

$34 \times 11 = 374$ $238 \times 11 = 2,618$
$1,655 \times 11 = 18,205$ $44,475 \times 11 = 489,225$

TO MAKE A SECRET CODE.

A	B	C	D	E	F	G	H	I	J	K	L	M
1	2	3	4	5	6	7	8	9	10	11	12	13

N	O	P	Q	R	S	T	U	V	W	X	Y	Z
14	15	16	17	18	19	20	21	22	23	24	25	26

Substitute the number for the letter.

Example:

2085   20920125   156   208919   2151511   919
2085   131793   156   142113251819

Solution:

The title of this book is *The Magic of Numbers.*

SECTION NINE

GEOMETRICAL PUZZLES

For answers, *see* SECTION ELEVEN, p. 59.

58. Where has the additional square inch come from in the two diagrams below?

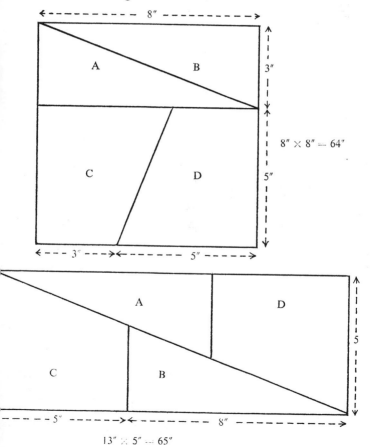

$8'' \times 8'' = 64''$

$13'' \times 5'' = 65''$

To divide a square into five equal squares or twenty equal triangles.

In the square ABCD bisect the sides at E, F, G, H, join AE, BF, CG, and DH, and then complete the diagram.

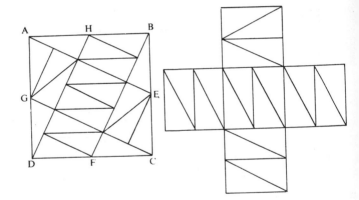

59. Using only 8 straight lines, how can you make 2 squares and 4 right-angle triangles?

To divide a square into three equal squares.

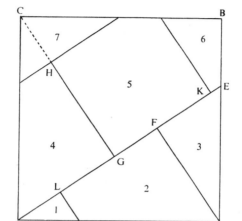

In the square ABCD, AE is half the diagonal and AF and CG are perpendiculars to DE. GH, GK, FL and AF are equal. The remaining lines are perpendiculars to the lines they intersect at H, K, and L respectively.

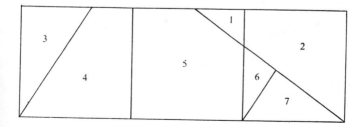

To make two squares and four equal triangles out of a rectangle measuring five inches by one inch.

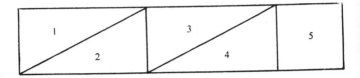

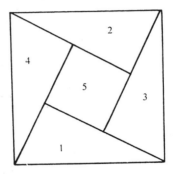

60. How many squares in this figure?

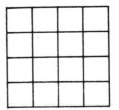

61. How many triangles of any size in this star?

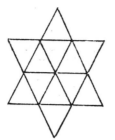

62.

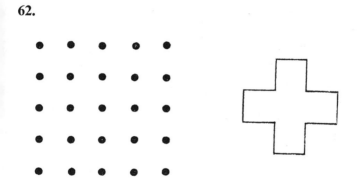

Join up the dots so as to make a cross like the one above, with five dots remaining inside the cross and eight dots outside the cross (*i.e.*, dots not used in the making of the cross).

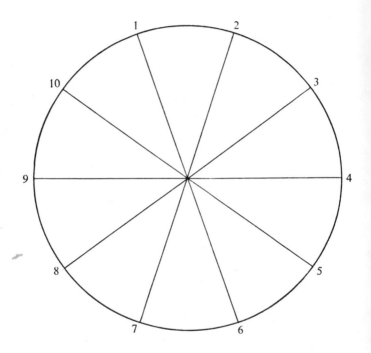

63. Rearrange the positions of the numbers 1 to 10 so that the sum of any two adjacent numbers is equal to the sum of the pair of numbers at the opposite ends of the diameters.

MAGIC SQUARES, CIRCLES, AND TRIANGLES

8	1	6
3	5	7
4	9	2

Horizontally
Vertically } adds up to 15
Diagonally

18	1	24	7	15
5	23	6	14	17
22	10	13	16	4
9	12	20	3	21
11	19	2	25	8

Horizontally
Vertically } adds up to 65
Diagonally

64. Using the numbers from 1 to 16 only once, arrange them as a Magic Square so that they add up to 34 horizontally, vertically, and diagonally.

65. Using the numbers 1, 2, 3, 10, 11, 12, 19, 20, and 21, place one of them in each square so as to form a Magic Square of 33.

Bordered Magic Square using numbers 1–36 inclusive

2	36	31	27	8	7
34	11	25	24	14	3
32	22	16	17	19	5
9	18	20	21	15	28
4	23	13	12	26	33
30	1	6	10	29	35

The complete square vertically, horizontally, and diagonally adds up to 111.

The inner square vertically, horizontally, and diagonally adds up to 74.

Magic Square in compartments using numbers 1–64 inclusive

1	63	62	4	9	55	54	12
60	6	7	57	52	14	15	49
8	58	59	5	16	50	51	13
61	3	2	64	53	11	10	56
17	47	46	20	25	39	38	28
44	22	23	41	36	30	31	33
24	42	43	21	32	34	35	29
45	19	18	48	37	27	26	40

Each compartment vertically, horizontally, and diagonally adds up to 130.
Side by side the same in every direction will be 260.

Benjamin Franklin (1706–90), using the numbers 1–256, compiled "The Magic of Magic Squares".

200	217	232	249	8	25	40	57	72	89	104	121	136	153	168	185
58	39	26	7	250	231	218	199	186	167	154	135	122	103	90	71
198	219	230	251	6	27	38	59	70	91	102	123	134	155	166	187
60	37	28	5	252	229	220	197	188	165	156	133	124	101	92	69
201	216	233	248	9	24	41	56	73	88	105	120	137	152	169	184
55	42	23	10	247	234	215	202	183	170	151	138	119	106	87	74
203	214	235	246	11	22	43	54	75	86	107	118	139	150	171	182
53	44	21	12	245	236	213	204	181	172	149	140	117	108	85	76
205	212	237	244	13	20	45	52	77	84	109	116	141	148	173	180
51	46	19	14	243	238	211	206	179	174	147	142	115	110	83	78
207	210	239	242	15	18	47	50	79	82	111	114	143	146	175	178
49	48	17	16	241	240	209	208	177	176	145	144	113	112	81	80
196	221	228	253	4	29	36	61	68	93	100	125	132	157	164	189
62	35	30	3	254	227	222	195	190	163	158	131	126	99	94	67
194	223	226	255	2	31	34	63	66	95	98	127	130	159	162	191
64	33	32	1	256	225	224	193	192	161	160	129	128	97	96	65

The sum of each column vertically or horizontally is 2,056. Every half-column vertically or horizontally adds up to 1,028.

Half a diagonal ascending added to half a diagonal descending makes 2,056, taking these half-diagonals from the ends of any side of the square to the middle of it.

The four corner numbers in the great square added to the four numbers in the center make 1,028.

The numbers in any square made up of 16 of the small squares (*i.e.*, 4 × 4) will add up to 2,056.

The sum of the numbers in any 2 × 2 small squares will be 514.

The Magic of Magic Squares (2)

200	217	232	249	8	25	40	57	72	89	104	121	136	153	168	185
58	39	26	7	250	231	218	199	186	167	154	135	122	103	90	71
198	219	230	251	6	27	38	59	70	91	102	123	134	155	166	187
60	37	28	5	252	229	220	197	188	165	156	133	124	101	92	69
201	216	233	248	9	24	41	56	73	88	105	120	137	152	169	184
55	42	23	10	247	234	215	202	183	170	151	138	119	106	87	74
203	214	235	246	11	22	43	54	75	86	107	118	139	150	171	182
53	44	21	12	245	236	213	204	181	172	149	140	117	108	85	76
205	212	237	244	13	20	45	52	77	84	109	116	141	148	173	180
51	46	19	14	243	238	211	206	179	174	147	142	115	110	83	78
207	210	239	242	15	18	47	50	79	82	111	114	143	146	175	178
49	48	17	16	241	240	209	208	177	176	145	144	113	112	81	80
196	221	228	253	4	29	36	61	68	93	100	125	132	157	164	189
62	35	30	3	254	227	222	195	190	163	158	131	126	99	94	67
194	223	226	255	2	31	34	63	66	95	98	127	130	159	162	191
64	33	32	1	256	225	224	193	192	161	160	129	128	97	96	65

Half a diagonal descending plus half a diagonal ascending equals 2,056, taking these half-diagonals from the ends of any side of the square to the middle of it.

Magic Circle using the numbers 1–61 inclusive

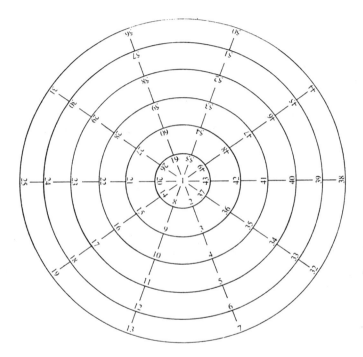

Numbers in each circumference add up to 315.
Numbers in each diameter add up to 379.
Numbers on the left-hand side of the diagram
increase by one from the center to the circumference.
Numbers on the right-hand side of the diagram
decrease by one from the center to the circumference.
Numbers in the circumference increase by six.

Magic Circle using the numbers 12–75 inclusive

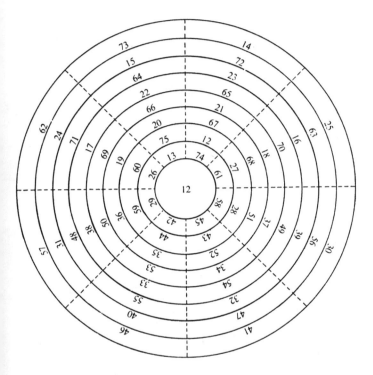

Numbers in each of the circles add up to 360.

Numbers in each radius together with the central number 12 add up to 360.

The numbers in half of any of the radii plus half the central number add up to 180.

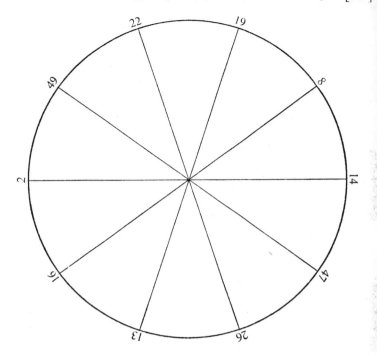

The sum of the squares of any two adjacent numbers is equal to the sum of the squares of the two numbers diametrically opposite to them. Thus:

$2^2 + 49^2 = 47^2 + 14^2$ $\qquad$ $4 + 2,401 = 2,405$
$\qquad\qquad\qquad\qquad\qquad\qquad = 2,209 + 196 = 2,405$

$49^2 + 22^2 = 26^2 + 47^2$ $\qquad$ $2,401 + 484 = 2,885$
$\qquad\qquad\qquad\qquad\qquad\qquad = 676 + 2,209 = 2,885$

$22^2 + 19^2 = 13^2 + 26^2$ $\qquad$ $484 + 361 = 845$
$\qquad\qquad\qquad\qquad\qquad\qquad = 169 + 676 = 845$

$19^2 + 8^2 = 16^2 + 13^2$ $\qquad$ $361 + 64 = 425$
$\qquad\qquad\qquad\qquad\qquad\qquad = 256 + 169 = 425$

$8^2 + 14^2 = 2^2 + 16^2$ $\qquad$ $64 + 196 = 260$
$\qquad\qquad\qquad\qquad\qquad\qquad = 4 + 256 = 260$

66.

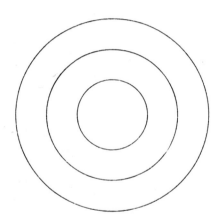

Using the above diagram as a pattern, make a Magic Circle with the numbers 1–31 inclusive.

A Magic Triangle

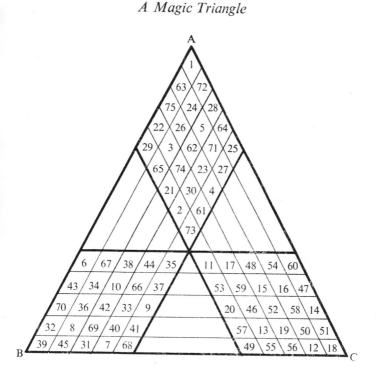

Any line down from A to B *or* A to C will total 380.
Any line across from B to C will also total 380.
Any line containing 5 figures in the above groups will total 190.

SECTION ELEVEN

SOLUTIONS

---

1. $1 = \dfrac{35}{70} + \dfrac{148}{296}$.

2. $100 = 50 + 49\frac{1}{2} + \dfrac{38}{76}$.

3. $31 = 3^3 + 3 + \dfrac{3}{3}$.

4. XIII. The top part is VIII = 8.

5. $\begin{array}{l} 987,654,321 = 45 \\ 123,456,789 = 45 \\ \hline 864,197,532 = 45 \end{array}$

6. II divided by V = M = 1,000.

7. $\dfrac{9,327}{18,654}$

8. $\begin{array}{r} 98,765 \\ 1,234 \\ \hline 99,999 \end{array}$

9. A pound of feathers is heavier than a pound of gold because feathers are weighed by the avoirdupois pound which consists of 16 ounces, while gold, being a precious metal, is weighed by the troy pound which contains only 12 ounces (5,760 grams).

10. TEN

11. NIL

12. $888 + 88 + 8 + 8 + 8.$

13. $44 + 44 + 4 + 4 + 4.$

14. $444 + 444 + 44 + 44 + 4 + 4 + 4 + 4 + 4 + 4.$

15. $99 + \dfrac{99}{99}$

16. Six dozen dozen $\;\;= 6 \times 12 \times 12 = 864.$
Half a dozen dozen $= 6 \times 12 \qquad\quad = \;\; 72.$

17. $22 + 2 = 24.$

18. $8 - \dfrac{8}{8} = 7.$

19. Tom had 5 marbles and Henry had 7 marbles.

20. 11 minutes, as the twelfth piece does not require sawing.

21. The farmer had 210 sheep.

$$\frac{1}{5}(42) + \frac{1}{6}(35) + \frac{1}{7}(30) = \frac{107}{210}$$

22. The fraction is 1/2 or 5/10. One fifth of 5/10 times 2 is 2/10, and multiplied by 1/2, equals 1/10.

23. At each of the 25 stations passengers can get tickets for any of the other 24 stations. Therefore the number of different tickets required is $25 \times 24 = 600$.

24. The boy solved 40 problems correctly and received $4.00, and paid his father the same amount for those not correct.

25. There is nothing to explain because 80 minutes is the same as 1 hour 20 minutes.

26. 12.

27. 36. $3 \times 6 = 18$, $18 \times 2 = 36$.

28. 27. $2 + 7 = 9$, $9 \times 3 = 27$.

29. The whole brick weighs 3 lb.

30. She had 143 eggs to begin with.

1st customer bought 72 eggs ($71\frac{1}{2} + \frac{1}{2}$) leaving 71.
2nd " " 36 eggs ($35\frac{1}{2} + \frac{1}{2}$) leaving 35.
3rd " " 18 eggs ($17\frac{1}{2} + \frac{1}{2}$) leaving 17.
4th " " 9 eggs ($8\frac{1}{2} + \frac{1}{2}$) leaving 8 eggs over.

31. The brick weighs 12 lb.

32. *Weights of 1, 2, 4, 8, 16, and 32 lb.*

Weight required in lb.	Weights used (lb.)	Weight required in lb.	Weights used (lb.)	Weight required in lb.	Weights used (lb.)
1	1	22	16 + 4 + 2	43	32 + 8 + 2 + 1
2	2	23	16 + 8 − 1	44	32 + 8 + 4
3	1 + 2	24	16 + 8	45	32 + 8 + 4 + 1
4	4	25	16 + 8 + 1	46	32 + 8 + 4 + 2
5	4 + 1	26	16 + 8 + 2	47	32 + 16 − 1
6	4 + 2	27	16 + 8 + 2 + 1	48	32 + 16
7	8 − 1	28	32 − 4	49	32 + 16 + 1
8	8	29	32 − (2 + 1)	50	32 + 16 + 2
9	8 + 1	30	32 − 2	51	32 + 16 + 2 + 1
10	8 + 2	31	32 − 1	52	32 + 16 + 4
11	8 + 2 + 1	32	32	53	32 + 16 + 4 + 1
12	8 + 4	33	32 + 1	54	32 + 16 + 4 + 2
13	8 + 4 + 1	34	32 + 2	55	32 + 16 + 8 − 1
14	16 − 2	35	32 + 2 + 1	56	32 + 16 + 8
15	16 − 1	36	32 + 4	57	32 + 16 + 8 + 1
16	16	37	32 + 4 + 1	58	32 + 16 + 8 + 2
17	16 + 1	38	32 + 4 + 2	59	32 + 16 + 8 + 2 + 1
18	16 + 2	39	32 + 8 − 1	60	32 + 16 + 8 + 4
19	16 + 2 + 1	40	32 + 8	61	32 + 16 + 8 + 4 + 1
20	16 + 4	41	32 + 8 + 1	62	32 + 16 + 8 + 4 + 2
21	16 + 4 + 1	42	32 + 8 + 2	63	32 + 16 + 8 + 4 + 2 + 1

33. *Weights of* 1, 3, 9, *and* 27 *lb.*

Weight required in lb.	Weights used (lb.)	Weight required in lb.	Weights used (lb.)
1	1	21	27 + 3 − 9
2	3 − 1	22	27 + 3 + 1 − 9
3	3	23	27 − (3 + 1)
4	3 + 1	24	27 − 3
5	9 − (3 + 1)	25	27 + 1 − 3
6	9 − 3	26	27 − 1
7	9 + 1 − 3	27	27
8	9 − 1	28	27 + 1
9	9	29	27 + 3 − 1
10	9 + 1	30	27 + 3
11	9 + 3 − 1	31	27 + 3 + 1
12	9 + 3	32	27 + 9 − (3 + 1)
13	9 + 3 + 1	33	27 + 9 − 3
14	27 − (9 + 3 + 1)	34	27 + 9 + 1 − 3
15	27 − (9 + 3)	35	27 + 9 − 1
16	27 + 1 − (9 + 3)	36	27 + 9
17	27 − (9 + 1)	37	27 + 9 + 1
18	27 − 9	38	27 + 9 + 3 − 1
19	27 + 1 − 9	39	27 + 9 + 3
20	27 + 3 − (9 + 1)	40	27 + 9 + 3 + 1

34. He paid $500 for one machine and $750 for the other one, a total of $1,250 in all.

He sold one for $600, losing 20%, and the other for $600, gaining 20%, making $1,200 altogether. His total loss therefore was $50.

35. The farmer would have to pay $167,772.15.

1st nail cost	1
2nd nail cost	2
3rd nail cost	4
4th nail cost	8
5th nail cost	16
6th nail cost	32
7th nail cost	64
8th nail cost	128
9th nail cost	256
10th nail cost	512
11th nail cost	1,024
12th nail cost	2,048
13th nail cost	4,096
14th nail cost	8,192
15th nail cost	16,384
16th nail cost	32,768
17th nail cost	65,536
18th nail cost	131,072
19th nail cost	262,144
20th nail cost	524,288
21st nail cost	1,048,576
22nd nail cost	2,097,152
23rd nail cost	4,194,304
24th nail cost	8,388,608

16,777,215 cents
or $167,772.15

36. There were   5 men each receiving $3 = $15.
There were 25 women each receiving $2 = $50.
There were 70 juniors each receiving   50¢ = $35.

37. The bottle cost $1.05, and the cork 5¢.

38. The dervish puts his own horse with the other seventeen, making eighteen horses in all. He then gives half to the eldest son—*i.e.*, 9 horses. The next son receives one-third—*i.e.*, 6 horses, and the youngest son gets one-ninth—*i.e.*, 2 horses. He then takes his own horse back again.

VESSEL	AMOUNT OF WINE IN EACH VESSEL BY STAGES							
	1	2	3	4	5	6	7	8
8 quart cask	8	3	3	6	6	1	1	4
5 quart jug	0	5	2	2	0	5	4	4
3 quart jug	0	0	3	0	2	2	3	0

39. *Stage* 1. He fills the 5-quart jug, leaving 3 quarts in the cask.

    2. He then fills the 3-quart jug from the 5-quart jug, so he has 3 quarts left in the cask, 3 quarts in the 3-quart jug, and 2 quarts in the 5-quart jug.

    3. He pours the contents of the 3-quart jug back into the cask, which then has 6 quarts.

    4. He pours the 2 quarts from the 5-quart jug into the 3-quart jug.

    5. He fills the 5-quart jug from the cask, leaving 1 quart remaining in the cask.

    6. He fills the 3-quart jug from the 5-quart jug. He then has 1 quart in the cask, 4 quarts in the 5-quart jug, and 3 quarts in the 3-quart jug.

    7. He pours the contents of the 3-quart jug into the cask.

    8. He then finishes up with 4 quarts in the cask and 4 quarts in the 5-quart jug.

40. She received 5 two-cent stamps, 30 one-cent stamps, and 7 five-cent stamps.

41.
        Raise of $30 *yearly*

1st year $100 + $100 = $200
2nd " $115 + $115 = $230
3rd " $130 + $130 = $260
4th " $145 + $145 = $290

        Raise of $10 *each half-year*

1st year $100 + $110 = $210
2nd " $120 + $130 = $250
3rd " $140 + $150 = $290
4th " $160 + $170 = $330

Addition

42.   2   4   7   11   16   22   29   37
          (+ 2   + 3   + 4   + 5   + 6   + 7   + 8)

43.   2   5   10   17   26   37   50   65
          (+ 3   + 5   + 7   + 9   + 11   + 13   +15)

Subtraction

44. 180   175   165   150   130   105   75   40
          (− 5   − 10   − 15   − 20   − 25   − 30 − 35)

45. 254   252   248   240   224   192   128   0
          (− 2   − 4   − 8   − 16   − 32   − 64 − 128)

Multiplication

46.   2   4   8   16   32   64   128   256

47.   2   4   12   48   240   1,440 10,080 80,640
          (× 2   × 3   × 4   × 5   × 6   × 7   × 8)

Division

48. 32   16   8   4   2   <u>1</u> $\frac{1}{2}$ $\frac{1}{4}$

49. 2,187   729   243   81   27   <u>9</u>   <u>3</u>   <u>1</u>

Addition

50. 1,234
4,321
$\overline{5,555}$

51. 111
234
342
312
$\overline{999}$

Subtraction

52. 5,478
4,367
$\overline{1,111}$

53. 6,258
5,743
$\overline{515}$

Multiplication

54.   38
39
$\overline{342}$
1,140
$\overline{1,482}$

55. 3,456
789
$\overline{31,104}$
276,480
2,419,200
$\overline{2,726,784}$

Division

56. 50)1900(38
150
$\overline{400}$
400
$\overline{\cdots}$

57. 215)37195(173
215
$\overline{1569}$
1505
$\overline{645}$
645
$\overline{\cdots}$

58.

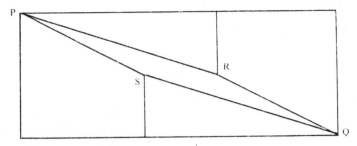

The edges of the four pieces of paper do not actually lie along the diagonal PQ, but form the parallelogram PSQR, the area of which is the elusive 65th square inch.

59.

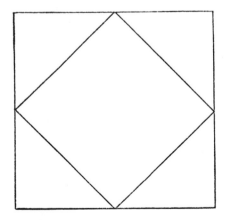

60. 30 squares.

61. 20 triangles.

62.

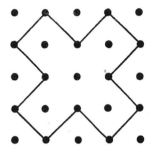

Five dots are inside the cross, while eight dots remain outside.

63.

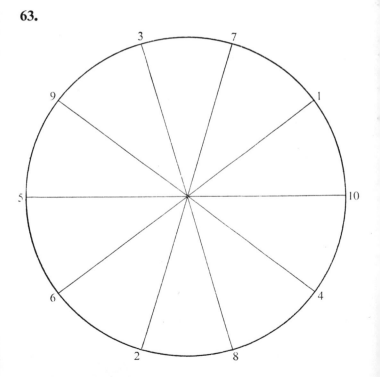

64.

16	2	3	13
5	11	10	8
9	7	6	12
4	14	15	1

1	12	7	14
8	13	2	11
10	3	16	5
15	6	9	4

65.

20	1	12
3	11	19
10	21	2

66.

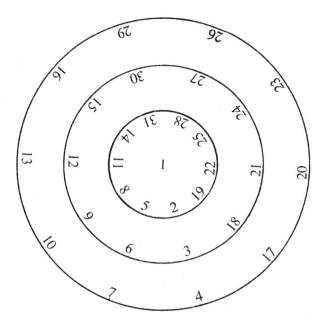

Numbers in each circumference add up to 165.
Numbers in each diameter add up to 100.

N.B. The numbers in the circumferences increase according to the number of circles. In the above there are three circles, therefore the numbers in the circumferences increase by three. Similarly, by four, five, or six, etc., where the same number of circles are used to note the Magic Circle.

QUALITY PAPERBACK BOOKS
Designed to Instruct and Entertain
Each book written by an expert in his field

Acting and Stage Movement, 95¢
Aeromodeling, $1.45
Amateur Psychologist's
    Dictionary, 95¢
Antique Furniture for the Smaller
    Home, 95¢
Archery, 95¢
Art of Riding, 95¢
Astrology, 95¢
Boy or Girl? Names for Every
    Child, 95¢
Cheiro's Book of Numbers, 95¢
Cheiro's Palmistry for All, 95¢
Cheiro's When Were You Born?, 95¢
Complete Guide to Palmistry, 95¢
Drama, 95¢
Find Your Job and Land It, 95¢
Fitness After Forty, $1.45
Gift Wrapping, 95¢
Golf at a Glance, 95¢
Guide to Personality Through
    Handwriting, $1.45
Health Foods and Herbs, 95¢
Heart Disease and High Blood
    Pressure, 95¢
Home Brewing Without Failures, 95¢
How to Be Healthy With Yoga, 95¢
How to Beat Personality Tests, $1.45
How to Train for Track and Field, 95¢
How to Win at Gin Rummy, 95¢
Instant Etiquette for
    Businessmen, 95¢
Judo and Self Defense, 95¢
Knots and Splices, 95¢

Laughter in a Damp Climate, $1.45
Lawn Tennis, 95¢
Magic of Numbers, 95¢
Manual of Sex and Marriage, $1.45
Mas Oyama's Karate, 95¢
Muscle Building for Beginners, 95¢
Mushroom Recipes, $1.45
131 Magic Tricks for Amateurs, 95¢
Painting and Drawing, 95¢
Practical Guide to Antique
    Collecting, 95¢
Production & Staging of Plays, 95¢
Profitable Poker, $1.45
Public Speaking, $1.45
Radio Astronomy and Building Your
    Own Telescope, 95¢
Remembering Made Easy, 95¢
Sailing Step by Step, 95¢
Shakespeare in the Red, 95¢
She Looks at Sex, 95¢
Slipped Discs, 95¢
Stamp Collecting for Fun and
    Profit, $1.45
Stomach Ulcers, 95¢
Student's Guide, $1.45
Successful Winemaking at Home, 95¢
3 Great Classics, $1.45
Upholstery, 95¢
Wake Up and Write, 95¢
Weightlifting & Weight Training, 95¢
Whole Truth About Allergy, 95¢
Woodturning, 95¢
You and Your Dog, 95¢
You Can Find a Fortune, $1.45
Your Allergic Child, $1.45

All books are also available in cloth-bound library editions at $2.50 and $3.50. If your bookstore is out of stock on any of the above titles, you can order books directly from ARC BOOKS, Inc., 219 Park Avenue South, New York, N.Y. 10003. Enclose check or money order for list price of books plus 10¢ per book for postage and handling. No C.O.D.